(C) 2021

The Counting Caterpillar
by
Debra E. Johnson
Illustrated by Raymond Sanders

This book is dedicated to the loves of my life, my husband Douglas and our daughters Zoe' and Zuri. Douglas has always encouraged me to follow my passion. Zoe' and Zuri were my very first students and are truly the inspiration for the content of this book. It has taken me 10 years to complete this book and they have supported every effort that I have made to get this book through to completion.

I am also grateful for my friends Kevin Edwards and Kim Bright who encouraged me to cross this task off of my vanishing bucket list.

The Counting Caterpillar visits the Caterpillar Clubhouse for a day of fun counting.

Let's inch inside...Hi kids: I have a numberlicious poem for us to do together as one.

Get ready for some counting fun.

one

Counting Caterpillar Counting

I see a big yellow sun.

Counting Caterpillar Counting

A Cheerio for me and a
Cheerio for you.

three

Counting Caterpillar Counting

Car horns blowing
Beep. Beep. Beep.

Counting Caterpillar Counting

Cookies falling on the floor.

five

Counting Caterpillar Counting

Baby Bees playing in the hive.

Counting Caterpillar Counting

Lollipops, Lollipops lick, lick, lick.

seven

Counting Caterpillar Counting

Red balloons floating up
to heaven.

eight

Counting Caterpillar Counting

Black birds sitting on a gate.

nine

Counting Caterpillar Counting

Little ducks walking in a line.

ten

Counting Caterpillar Counting

Counting all my caterpillar friends.

1 2 3 4 5 6 7 8 9 10

I will come back another day
and we can do it again.

Be good until next time......

A Note from
The Traveling Caterpillar

Dear Reader,

I hope that you have enjoyed learning how to count to 10 with me. Reach out and let me know how much you enjoyed this book. If you want to journey with me and learn your colors, numbers, letters, or sight words, be sure to get our other books on these subjects. Check out some of the students who are putting this book into practice.

www.djscaterpillarclubhouse.com
cchcorresponds@gmail.com

About the
Author

Debra Johnson is a native of Atlanta, GA. She holds a Bachelor's degree in Bible/Music. She also holds a Master's degree in Early Childhood Education with an emphasis on Literacy and Reading. She is married and the biological mother of 2 daughters, but a surrogate to many in the classroom.

While teaching kindergarten and second grade in the public school system for a few years, she made the decision to leave the public sector and open up the Caterpillar Clubhouse Academy & Daycare where they "Teach Toddlers to Read". She wanted to dedicate the next stage of her educational career partnering with parents and providing a safe and developmentally appropriate environment for toddlers starting at age 18 months to the age of 4. Her focus would be to provide a stimulating early care and educational experience which promotes each child's ability to learn and read as they are developing as well as shape their social/emotional, physical, and cognitive development.

Made in the USA
Columbia, SC
20 September 2021